INDY 500

by Anabel Dean
Teacher
Redding, California

BENEFIC PRESS
Westchester, Illinois

RACING WHEELS SERIES

Hot Rod

Destruction Derby

Drag Race

Stock Car Race

Road Race

Indy 500

Library of Congress
Number 72-170775

Printed in the United States of America

CONTENTS

Chapter

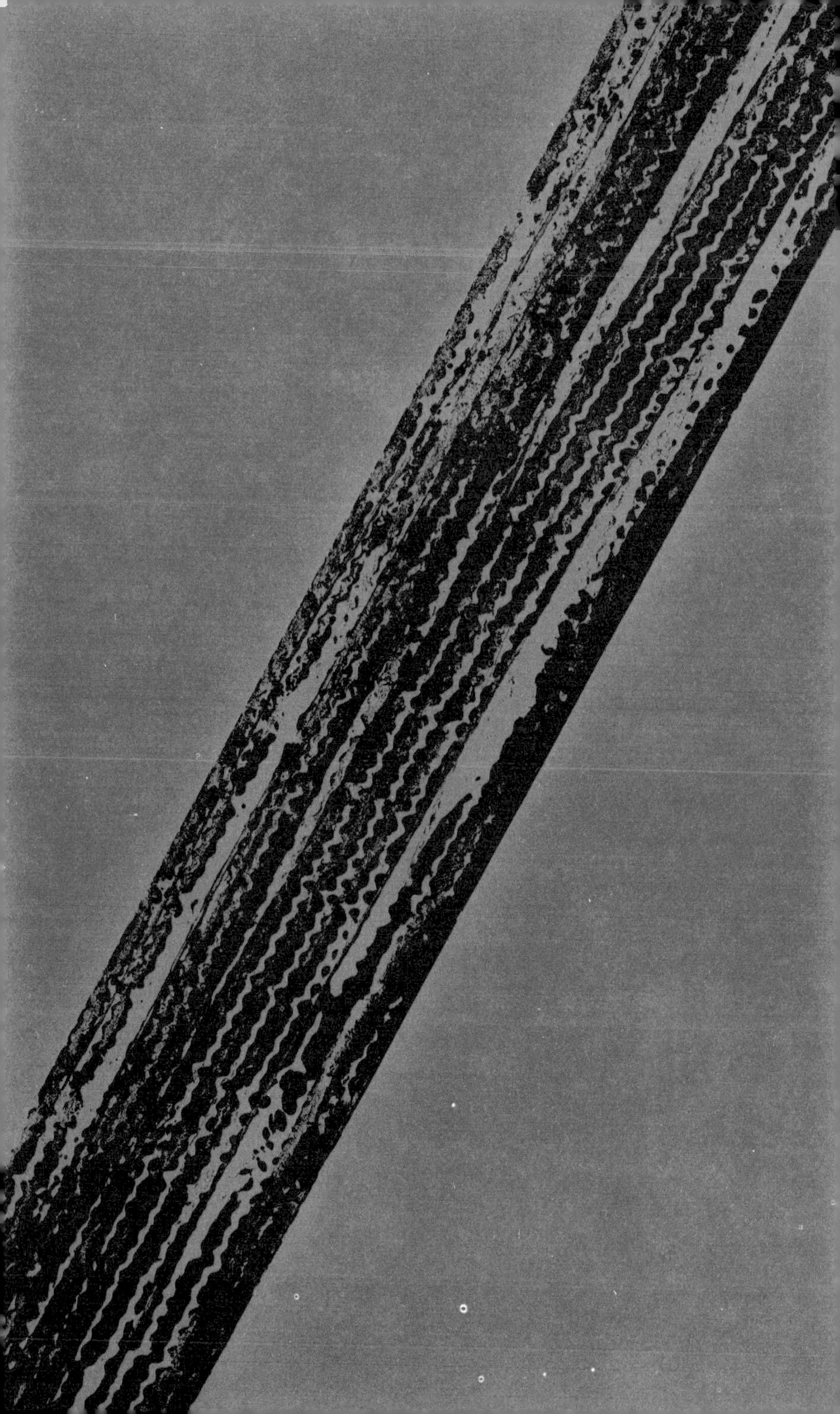

1

Road Race Driver

Woody Woods put his Lotus into a drift around the next wide turn. Brian ("Goggles") Mahoney in a Ferrari was right in back of him. Woody was using all of his skill from two years of road racing to try and stay ahead of "Goggles" Mahoney. Woody knew that the Ferrari Mahoney was driving was much faster than any other car on the track. It was a Ferrari prototype 312P.

"They shouldn't have let that Ferrari be in this race," thought Woody. "That car isn't in the same class as the others in this race." Woody thought that the track judges had only let that Ferrari be in the road race because it was driven by Brian Mahoney, the big track racer from Indianapolis. The stands were full of people who had come to see Mahoney race today.

When the two cars came into the straightaway, the Ferrari caught up with Woody. Woody knew that his Blue Wasp could go ahead on the next turn. Mahoney could not take these turns as fast as Woody could.

"This is Mahoney's first road race in some time. If I don't beat him, I'll never hear the end of it," Woody said to himself.

Brian Mahoney was a well known track racer. The newspapers called him "Goggles" because he was one of the only drivers who still wore goggles instead of a face-shield attached to the helmet. He had raced in many track races and had even raced at Indianapolis the last two years. Last year he had placed second in the "500." Mahoney was a friend of Buck Brown's, and Buck had talked him into coming here to be in a road race. Woody knew that Buck wanted Mahoney to be in this race so Mahoney could beat Woody.

Woody had seen Mahoney on T.V. the day before. It made Woody angry to think about it. Mahoney had told the reporter that after driving at Indianapolis, driving in a road race would be simple. He said that he, Brian Mahoney, would win. Woody wanted to show him that road racing was not as easy as it looked. But Woody did not know that they would let him use such a powerful car. That machine had power to burn.

STP
77

"He can't take the corners fast enough in that car though," said Woody to himself. "I can still beat him if the Blue Wasp holds up."

The two cars roared down the straightaway in front of the stands. There were more people here today than had ever been at this course before. The stands were jammed. The papers had been saying that a driver from Indy named Brian ("Goggles") Mahoney was out to give Woody Woods a beating.

Woody had won many road races in the last two years. Many of the people in the stands were cheering for Woody. They knew him or had seen him race before. Others were yelling for Mahoney because he was a big name race car driver, and he was always in the newspapers.

The Ferrari pulled ahead as they went down the straightaway. "I'll be ahead after this next turn," thought Woody.

Woody downshifted and braked as he came up to the next turn. He pushed the brake pedal to the floor. It felt like his brakes were almost gone.

Woody began to slide around the turn going much too fast. He turned the wheel and tried to use his brakes to control the slide. The car came out of the turn but too late. Woody had lost time taking it so wide. He was going too slow to pick up speed now.

Woody went down the straightaway too slow. The Ferrari pulled ahead of him. Woody downshifted and tried the brakes again. At the next turn, the brakes were almost gone.

Woody knew there were only two laps to go. What a time for his brakes to go out! He could finish the race at a slower speed and lose, or he could speed up and maybe lose control and crash into another car or some of the people standing near the track.

Woody knew there was only one thing for him to do. He slowed down. "Goggles" Mahoney moved ahead of him. Woody finished second. Woody knew that the Blue Wasp was far enough ahead of the other cars so they could not catch up with him. He knew he could not catch up with Mahoney, though.

Woody did the next two laps at a much slower speed. By the time Woody had finished the race, Mahoney was in the winners circle with many people crowding around him.

2

Road Racing is Second Rate?

"IS ROAD RACING SECOND-RATE?" Woody Woods looked at the paper that Mr. House held up for him to see. "Would you look at that," yelled Mr. House. "Just look at that!"

Woody had just come into the House Racing Shop the morning after the road race. "Listen to this, Woody," said Mr. House, holding the paper up so Woody could see it. Woody didn't think he had ever seen Mr. House so angry about anything.

> "Brian (Goggles) Mahoney who placed second at Indianapolis last year, raced on our road racecourse yesterday. He showed Woody Woods, a driver from our town, how the championship drivers race. Woods did not even come close. After the race, when asked how hard the course was,

he said, 'It was easy. After driving at Indianapolis, this race was like kid's stuff. The best driver from around here, Woody Woods, couldn't keep pace with me. He may be a good driver around here but he couldn't even qualify at Indianapolis.' "

"How do you like that?" said Mr. House, dropping the paper. "Mahoney is making us look like boys racing little cars. I know Buck Brown is behind this. He's trying to get even with me. He's holding a grudge."

"Well, Mahoney *did* win," said Woody. "It won't do any good to tell the newspapers that my brakes gave out. Everyone would think I was saying that because I didn't win."

"Woody was driving a better race than Mahoney was," said Jeff. "I think Woody would have won if his brakes had held out."

"We can't say that," said Woody. "Anything could have happened. I had a good chance to beat him, but he went over the finish line first, and that's what it takes to win."

"This is going to be bad for business," said Mr. House. "Who will want to come to us for parts or racing equipment if the papers are saying that our cars or drivers are bush league? The Blue Wasp does not look like much of a car after being beaten by that Ferrari prototype," said Mr. House, as he shook his head slowly.

The next few days Woody just did not want to see anyone. Woody had always liked to go down to "Bonnie's", walk around and see the people he knew. They would stop him and ask about the last or the next road race he was in. Now all the people talked about was Brian Mahoney, how he had beaten Woody in the road race. They no longer thought Woody was much of a driver.

The next Saturday Woody was working on one of the few stock cars to come into the House Racing Shop this week. The bad showing in the race and the bad reports about it in the papers were keeping many people away from Mr. House's Racing Shop. Mr. House, Jeff, and Tap were all working around the shop that morning even if there was not too much to do.

"Hey, Woody," said someone behind him. "We just came to see you before we go."

Woody turned around to see that Buck and Brian Mahoney were in back of him. "Where are you going?" asked Woody.

"I have a few races left on the tour, and then I have to go to Indianapolis to start practicing for the '500'," said Mahoney. "I am going to come in first this year. There is something I wanted to see you about before I left, though."

"What is it?" asked Woody.

"Well, said Mahoney. "After seeing your setup here, I could see that you will never make it as a driver on the championship tour. Mr. House doesn't have that kind of money. But you could be a good pit worker. If you want to work in the pits for my racing team, you could come with us and even be in the pits at Indianapolis."

"You're close!" said Woody. "If I go to Indianapolis, it will be as a driver and not as your lackey! But I think I will stay with road racing. I think there is more challenge to it."

"There is no money in road racing, Woody," said Mahoney. "The big money is all at Indy."

"Maybe so," said Woody. "But road racing is my kind of racing."

"If you want to stay with this bush-league racing, it's all right with me," said Mahoney. "Don't try to race at Indy though or the big boys will run you off the track, Woody, my boy."

After Buck and Brian had gone, Mr. House came over to see what they had wanted. When Woody told him, he was very angry.

"So Mahoney will let you work as a helper!" said Mr. House. "That's good of him. The things those two have told the paper while they were here have hurt business, Woody. I have to do something, but I don't know what. What do you think, Woody?"

"I don't know what we can do," said Woody. "But I am tired of everyone thinking that I am not much of a driver."

"What Mahoney told you about the big money being at Indianapolis is right," said Mr. House. "You don't have to be first to win a lot of money. You know, Woody, if we were to qualify a car in the race at Indianapolis, we could win some money, and it would really help business if we placed."

"If we didn't place, it would hurt business," said Woody. "What's more, we don't have the kind of money to put a car into the race at Indy. You would need a driver with savvy, too, because I don't know anything about racing an Indy-type machine."

"I'll have time to think about it while I am in Chicago next week. I'm going to talk to the company that sells us racing parts. They might be interested," said Mr. House. "You watch things for me here while I am in Chicago."

3

The Offenhauser

"Woody! Woody Woods! Wait up."

Woody turned around to see who was calling him. He had just come from his last class of the day. Woody was not thinking about this class. He was thinking about the Indianapolis "500." Was Mahoney right about the Indy race? Was it harder than road racing? Woody knew that there were many crashes at Indianapolis because the cars went at such high speeds. Could it be he was afraid to race at Indy?

Woody turned around to see who was calling him. Ann House was running after him, dropping things as she ran. He watched her stop and run back to get something she had dropped. Woody had been working for Ann's father now for two years, and he and Ann had known each other for almost that long.

"What is it, Ann?" Woody asked as he walked back to help with her things.

"I have something to tell you," called Ann.

"What do you have to tell me?" asked Woody as they walked to Woody's car.

"Father wants to see you at the shop as soon as you're finished for the day," said Ann. "He has something to show you."

"Well, let's go then, Ann," said Woody.

Mr. House came out of the racing shop when Ann and Woody drove up. "I thought it was you, Woody," he said. "Wait and see what I got in Chicago."

Mr. House took them into the shop. He looked very happy about something. "From the way you look, I think it must have something to do with a new car," said Woody.

In the shop they could see something big that was all covered up. It was long and looked as if it could be a race car.

"The men from the company that makes the parts we sell here think we are afraid of Brian Mahoney and Indianapolis. They think we should do something about it," said Mr. House. "Bad business for me means bad business for them. So this company is going to put up money for the whole thing. I mean, they're going to pick up the whole tab."

"Father," said Ann. "Show us what is under that cover."

Mr. House took the cover off of the car. There was a long, powerful looking race car. It looked so powerful that Ann and Woody could only stare at it.

Woody looked at the powerful engine on the low car. It was a four cylinder turbocharged Offenhauser. He could see that the car was weighted on the left side so it would turn left only. This was the USAC championship car that had been made for only one race—the "500" at Indianapolis.

"It looks as if it could do well over 200 miles an hour," Woody said at last.

"It can go that fast. We'll have to set up the suspension, of course, but we have lots of time to fix it up," Mr. House said. "We have some good mechanics here."

"OK. I like everything about it," said Woody.

"Well, you are going to drive this car at Indianapolis this year," said Mr. House. "We are going to show Brian Mahoney and Buck Brown that my car and my road race driver can race and win, at the '500'."

"Mr. House," said Woody slowly. "We could lose, too. I have never driven a car like this and I have never driven at Indianapolis. If we don't qualify or I can't pass my test, it will hurt your business."

"That is a chance we will have to take," said Mr. House.

"But, Mr. House," said Woody, "I don't know if I can drive this car, and I don't know if I want to. I want to stay with road racing."

"You won't know if you can drive the car unless you try, Woody. You must try it."

"O.K. Mr. House. Let me try it out before I say I will drive it," said Woody. "But I am tired of everyone thinking I am afraid to drive at Indianapolis. I don't think it should take too long to get used to driving a car like this. With a little coaching, I can do it."

4

Turbocharged

R- r-r-r-r-r-r-r-r-r-r-r-r-r-o-o-o-o-o-ommmmm! The turbocharged machine roared around the track. The powerful car slid almost out of control as it took the turns. Woody was afraid to put the car into a drift. "Driving this car is like nothing I have ever tried before," said Woody to himself as he took the Queen Bee around another turn. "This car is tough to handle," said Woody to himself.

Woody had been practicing with the Queen Bee for two weeks. Woody had thought that it would be easy to get used to the car—it was not. Woody felt that the car had too much power for him to have control. If the car wasn't driven just right, it would not stay on the track. Woody could see that it would take a lot longer than he had thought for him to have control of this car.

Everyone at the House Racing Shop knew now that Woody would drive the Queen Bee at the Indianapolis speedway.

Woody was using an old race track to practice on. It wasn't much like the track at Indianapolis, and it wasn't as big around, but it was all they had to run on.

Mr. House, Jeff, Tap and Woody had worked on the Queen Bee for over a month now getting it ready to race. The car was now running very smoothly and was very fast. Woody almost felt that it was too fast.

After a few more laps, Woody pulled into the pits. Mr. House, Tap, Jeff, and Ann were with the pitcrew waiting for him. Mr. House wasn't too happy about something.

"Woody, that car will go faster than that," said Mr. House. "You're not driving it as fast as it will go. Open it up!"

"The car will go faster all right, Mr. House," said Woody. "But I'm not ready to open it up any more. This car is a lot harder to drive than any car I have driven before and this track just isn't big enough to handle speed that high.

After the practice runs were over for the day, Woody went back to town with Ann. "Woody," said Ann as she drove. "I have been thinking. Will you be ready to race that car in the '500' in two months?"

"That is what I was thinking about, too," said Woody. "There is a lot more to racing in the '500' than I had thought at first. Those cars are so fast that if you make one wrong move you've had it."

"There will be a lot of fast, powerful cars in that race," said Ann. "The drivers will be the best. If you don't think you are ready, Woody, don't do it. It would only take one good crash, and that would be it."

When they got back to the shop, they waited for the boys to get back with the Queen Bee. Woody helped them put the car away.

The next day, just Jeff, Tap, Woody, and the pitcrew took the Queen Bee out to the race track again. On the way out to the track Woody thought that he would try to drive the Queen Bee faster today.

First, Woody did a few laps to warm up the car. When he went by the pits the third time, he put his hand up. Jeff would start timing him now. Woody started faster laps.

Woody took the first turn at a faster speed than he had before. He tried to start a drift but had to brake hard. The turn was not banked enough for a good drift in this car.

"I will never get used to taking a turn in high," Woody said to himself. He made himself keep up his speed and tried to get a drift going in the second turn.

At first, Woody thought he was drifting all right. Then he could see that his speed was too much for this turn. He hit the brakes and tried to use the wheel to get himself out of the spin he knew was coming up. Now he was going around and around. There was a bang as the Queen Bee hit the wall. Woody was lucky. No one was hurt. Only a few pieces of the wheel rim had fallen off.

They all knew that this track was not big enough to handle the high speed of these cars. They had to get to "Indy," and soon.

5

On to Indianapolis

Down the highway went three cars, one in back of the other. The first one was the pickup truck pulling the Queen Bee. Jeff was driving it. The pickup was full of parts they would need for the race. Next came another truck. Tap was driving this truck, and Mr. House was with him. The truck was full of parts and tires they would need at the race.

Last in the line came Ann driving her car. Woody was with her. Mr. House would not let Woody drive on the way to Indianapolis. "You will get enough driving when we get to the Speedway," he said.

Woody felt better now that they were at last going to Indianapolis. "I am happy we are on our way," he said to Ann. "I want to try the Queen Bee out on the track there."

The next day they pulled into Indianapolis. Someone showed them where they could put their race car in Gasoline Alley. This was the place where the race cars were kept and worked on before the race. All the necessary tools were there.

They were all very happy to be at Indianapolis. The first thing they did was to go out to look at the track. There were big stands around it. Woody had never seen such big stands. The track in front of the stands was covered with bricks.

"I thought the whole track was made of brick," said Ann.

"It was at one time," said Woody. "But they have covered all of the bricks over now but the ones in front of the stands."

It was late by the time they had the race car, pickup and truck put away. They all got into Ann's car and went to town to find a place to stay. They would have to be at Indianapolis for about two months.

The next morning everyone but Ann was back at the race track very early.

"Come on, Woody," said Mr. House. "We are going to take a long walk."

"Take a walk?" asked Woody. "Where are we going? I thought I came here to drive."

"We are going to walk the track so you will know it before you drive it," said Mr. House.

"Well, all right, I sure hope no one's driving on it," said Woody. He and Mr. House started out to walk the 2-½ mile long track.

As they walked, Mr. House talked to Woody. He showed him the way the wind came down through the stands and the way there was more wind at some corners than at others. They looked at the banked turns and at the smooth straightaway of the track.

Woody began to be happy about driving the Queen Bee here. "I have never driven on a track this big before," he said.

When they got back to the car, Woody was very tired from all of the walking. They saw that someone had put three big pieces of tape on the top of the spoiler.

"Who put that tape on our spoiler?" asked Mr. House.

"One of the race track officials," said Jeff. "We have to keep the tape on the car until Woody passes his driving test."

"What did he say, Jeff?" asked Woody.

"The official said that every driver had to take a test before he could race if he had never driven in the '500' before," said Jeff. "We have to keep the tape on until you pass your test so the other drivers can watch out for you."

"Oh, good," said Woody. "They want everyone to know I have never raced here before."

"Let's go get something to eat now," said Mr. House. "We can talk more about it then. You can practice in the Offy after we eat."

While they were eating, Jeff and Tap told them about the many fast racing cars they had seen in Gasoline Alley.

When they got back to the race track, it was open for practice. Some of the drivers who had not driven at Indy before were taking their driving tests. Ann had come out to watch, too.

"Are you going to take your driving test today?" asked Tap.

"Not me," said Woody. "I would never pass it. I want to practice for some time before I take that test."

They pushed the Queen Bee over to the track. Woody put on his helmet and got in. Tap and Jeff brought up the starter. They fastened the starter up, and the engine started with a roar. While Woody waited for the flagman to give the signal that the track was open, he watched the race cars roar by. Woody didn't know if he wanted to get out there with those fast cars. Some of them were doing 170 plus miles an hour.

Now the flagman signalled to Woody that he could go and he roared out on the track. You had to drive fast on this track, or you would be hit from behind by one of the cars.

Woody didn't drive any faster than he had to at first. He wanted to try to get used to this new track. By the time he got to the first turn, the car was doing 100 mph.

Woody had trouble taking the turns at this speed on the old track he had been practicing on. On these banked turns you didn't even know you were going around a corner.

Woody did about five more laps at about 100 miles an hour. This wasn't very fast for this track, but he wanted to get used to the track before he went any faster.

On the straight piece in front of the stand a black McLaren M16 zoomed by Woody. He could see a name painted on the side. It said, "Brian Mahoney."

"Well," said Woody, as he saw Mahoney's car zoom around the turn in front of him. "He'll be laughing at me when I get back

Woody did some more laps and then drove into the pits. The Queen Been wasn't running too well. As he pulled into the pits, Mr. House said, "Woody, you only did 110 miles an hour. We will never qualify, and you will never pass the driver's test if you can't go any faster than that. What's wrong with you?"

"Give me a little time," said Woody. "This is only the first time I have been on this track and the timing of the car is off."

Now Mahoney and Buck Brown came walking over. "Woody, you did the slowest laps that have been turned in here," said Brian with a laugh. "You might as well leave, now. You will never pass the driver's test. Why don't you stay with road racing?"

Woody turned and walked off. He had enough troubles. He didn't need Mahoney and Buck giving him a bad time. While Jeff worked at the timing, Woody was thinking. Now that he had seen how fast the cars went on this track he didn't know if he could drive that fast. How could he pass his driving test?

6

The Rookies' Test

Ann and Woody were driving out to the track the next morning. Woody was still feeling pretty tired, even though he slept late.

Mr. House, Woody, Jeff, and Tap had been working late taking the Queen Bee down the night before. They were afraid the long drive to Indianapolis had hurt the car. All the parts had been cleaned, and they were going to fix the car again this morning.

Mr. House, Tap, and Jeff had gone out to the track early. They wanted Woody to sleep late so he would be ready to practice again. Ann and Woody had stopped for a paper so they could check out some of the news of yesterday's practice. Ann had been reading a column near the bottom of the sports page.

"Listen to this, Woody," Ann said, after reading the paper some more.

"Woody Woods, the youngest driver trying to qualify here, did not do very well on his first day of practicing at Indianapolis. His car, a 4 cylinder turbocharged Offenhauser, was clocked at only 110.456 miles per hour. This is the slowest time of any car in any practice yet this year. It is the slowest time for anyone at Indy in a long time. Mr. Brian (Goggles) Mahoney told us yesterday that Mr. Woods looked uneasy at Indianapolis. Mr. Mahoney did not think that the Offenhauser would qualify for the '500' or that Mr. Woods would even pass the driver's test. 'Maybe next year,' said Brian Mahoney."

Woody tried not to let the things in the paper bother him. He had enough things to think about. When they got to Gasoline Alley, they found everyone there very busy. Every place you looked, pit crews were working.

"The Queen Bee is ready to go," called Tap as Woody and Ann came in. Some of the expert crewmen who worked for Mr. House had the car all fixed up again and tuned and timed. It was all set to go.

They took the Queen Bee over to the pits and Woody got ready to practice again. Woody started out slowly to get the car warmed up. He could feel that the car was running better today than it was yesterday.

After a few laps at slow speed, Woody opened the car up some. The roar was even louder, now. Then he began to look for the fastest line through the corners. The two turns after the straightaway were so close to each other that Woody could almost take them as one big turn. After a few laps, Jeff picked up the stop watch and began to time the Offenhauser as it picked up speed.

When Woody pulled off the track after going 30 laps, he found that his best time on the laps was about 125 miles an hour. That was better than yesterday, but it still wasn't fast enough to qualify or as fast as he would have to go when taking his driver's test. Woody would have to open up the engine even more.

After two weeks, he was getting better. His time was up to 145 miles an hour.

They practiced pit stops every day, too. A race can be won or lost on how long it takes a pit crew during a stop. The best pit crews could have a car back on the track in 20 seconds. Over and over they practiced putting fuel in the car, jacking it up, changing the tires, and cleaning off the little windshield. They found that they didn't need to change the left front tire. When the car went around the corners turning to the left all the time, this tire didn't get as much use as the other tires.

At first it took them a long time for a pit stop. They looked for faster and faster ways to do things. At last, they had it down to 25 seconds. They still needed more practice stops. In 25 seconds many cars would get ahead of them.

Every morning track officials talked to the drivers about the things they could and could not do in the race and while practicing. The officials told the new drivers about the test they would have to take before they could drive in the "500." Woody found that he would have to do ten laps at 140 miles an hour, ten laps at 145 miles an hour, ten laps at 150 miles an hour, and ten laps at 155 miles

an hour. These test laps showed if a driver could tell how fast he was going and if he could control his car at faster and faster speeds. There would be men at places around the track to watch the driver take his test. If the driver didn't do well at any of the speeds, he would not pass his test.

Woody practiced every day. Still he didn't know if he could pass his driver's test. Time was running out on Woody.

The next morning Woody knew he could not put it off any longer. After he got through practicing, he went over and talked to the track officials. He would have to take his driver's test the next day.

Woody didn't sleep much that night. All night long he kept thinking about taking his driving test.

Woody was out at the track early the next morning. It was a good day with little wind. It would be easier to pass his test on a day like this. Woody looked up at the stands as he drove to Gasoline Alley. There were quite a few people in the stands. Some people came to the stands every day to watch the drivers practice, take their driving tests, or do their qualifying runs.

Woody said to himself, "If I don't pass this test today, all those people will see me fail."

The House pit crew was in the pits. They had the Queen Bee ready to go. The race track officials were waiting for Woody. It was time to start. Woody took his time putting his helmet on and was slow about getting into the car. When he was ready, he looked at Ann, Tap, Jeff, and Mr. House who were watching him. He could not talk over the roar of the engine. Then he drove the car up to wait for the flagman to give him the signal that the track was now open.

Now the flagman brought the flag down and Woody roared out on the track. He could do a few laps to warm up and get ready for his test. Woody did five laps. By then his engine was warm, and his speed was up.

The Queen Bee was running good, too. Woody watched his speed as he drove. Now he was doing about 155 mph in the straightaway. Since he would have to go slower on the turns, his average time for the lap should be about 140 miles an hour.

The sixth time Woody went by the track official at the start-finish line, Woody put his hand up. Now his driver's test would start. The officials would start to time him.

Woody, like many race car drivers, was always a little afraid before a race or a test run. After he got started, he was fine. After the test started Woody felt calm. All he thought about at this time was taking this test and passing it.

Now the Queen Bee went into the first turn. Woody didn't downshift as he would do if he were in a road race. By now he knew how to drive this car on this track. He "backed off" the gas pedal, tapped the brakes lightly, and dove low into the turn, but stayed in high gear. The Queen Bee drifted through the turn. Woody gave the car more fuel for only a little while as he came out of one drift before he drifted into the next turn. On the straightaway, Woody gave the car more fuel and the Queen Bee roared ahead. Woody thought that he was getting good performance from his turbocharged machine.

Woody did ten laps as close to 140 miles per hour as he could. Then he speeded up a little. The wind had come up some and on one corner the wind made it hard for him to hold the Queen Bee in a drift. Still, Woody felt that he did the 145 mile per hour laps all right. Woody made the last turn and rushed into the straightaway.

Woody came into the pits for a stop after this part of his test was over. "How is the Queen Bee doing?" yelled Mr. House. Jeff and Tap put more fuel in the car and looked over the tires to see if they would last for 20 more laps. Their pit stops were getting faster.

Woody gave Mr. House the "thumbs-up" signal and shook his head yes before he took the car back out on the track. "I think we have got her the way we want her," said Mr. House.

Now Woody drove even faster. After two laps, he was doing 190 miles per hour in the straightaway. His lap speed should be only one or two miles off the speedy 150 mph.

By now Woody had worked out the cutoff places on each turn. He knew the places where he would "backoff" on the fuel, dive low into the turn, and start the drift. At this higher speed he had to touch the brakes a little on each turn, but not the way he would have used them in a road race.

In the straightaway in front of the stands, Woody opened the car up. The roar of the Queen Bee had some of the people standing up to see what car was going by.

Woody only had ten laps to do now at 155 miles per hour. If Woody could do these 10 laps as well as the other 30 laps, Woody felt that he would pass the driver's test.

Woody began to cut faster laps now. He took a few seconds off each turn then and opened the car up a little more on the straightaway. After five laps, Woody began to think that he was doing well on his 155 mile per hour laps. By the last few laps, Woody was going all out.

As Woody went into one turn on the next to last lap, the wind hit the Queen Bee. It was just as if someone had pushed the car around. The back of the car swung around, and for a second Woody thought the car would go into a spin. It was only by fast work on Woody's part that he kept the car from spinning. He had to hit the brakes and was going much slower into the next turn.

Woody lost some time on this lap. He tried to make up some of the time, but he did not think he went fast enough.

Woody drove into the pits, got out of the car, took off his helmet, and threw it on the ground.

"What is it? asked Mr. House. "What happened to you?"

"Now I've done it," said Woody. "I'll never pass my driver's test. I almost went into a spin on a turn. My time wasn't fast enough because of those last laps."

"Well, let's go over to the official's stand and get it over with," said Mr. House. "You were supposed to go there when the test was over, Woody. We have to know what they have to say about your driving."

All the track officials were standing around talking. The head judge was talking to the men who had been at all of the turns.

At first they didn't see Woody and the others. Then one of the officials said, "Come over here, Woods."

Woody walked over to the men. Now he would get the bad news. "You had a little trouble on one of your last turns, didn't you?" said the official. "Your time on the last ten laps was only 154.75 miles per hour. It should have been 155 miles per hour. But don't worry. That was close enough, so you have passed your driving test."

Now everyone was hitting Woody on the back and yelling, "Nice going, Woody!"

"Let's take the tape off the back of the Queen Bee," said Tap. "You have passed your test, Woody. Now we have to qualify."

7

Mahoney Qualifies

For the next few days, Woody could only practice a little while each day. Almost all day other rookie drivers were taking their driver's test. Many of those who took the test did not pass.

Each car and driver had to pass a qualifying test. Many more cars wanted to be in the race than there would be room for on the track. The drivers of over 90 cars wanted to be in the race but there would only be room for 33 cars. The cars to be in the Indianapolis "500" would be the cars with the fastest qualifying times. Each driver would do four laps to get the fastest average speed as he could. Each driver would have three chances to qualify. If a driver could not go fast enough to qualify, he could not be in the Indianapolis "500."

Every day the crew of the Queen Bee watched the qualifying laps for a while. Many of the cars went faster in these laps than they would go in the race. One day while they were watching the cars, Woody asked about this.

"It is because of the fuel they use in the qualifying runs," said Mr. House.

"Don't they use the same fuel in the time trials that they use in the race?" asked Woody.

"No," said Mr. House. "We will use a more powerful fuel for our qualifying runs. If we used that fuel for the race, the engine would get too hot or would burn out."

Twice Woody did four laps to try and qualify. Each time his time was not fast enough. Today they were watching some of the drivers do their qualifying laps. The next day Woody would have his last chance to try and qualify.

As they watched, they could hear the loud speaker say, "Brian Mahoney will now do his first qualifying laps."

Brian Mahoney, in his low streamlined McLaren M16, zoomed by on the track. Mahoney was a very fast driver, but not a safe one. He had been in many accidents. He did not like to have anyone pass him. Some of the people were standing up to watch him as he flashed by the stands the second time. He was something to watch. He was a very exciting driver.

Jeff began to time him, too. Mahoney took the turns as fast as he could and still stay on the track. When he went by the next time, Jeff looked at his watch.

"Boy," said Jeff. "That Mahoney is fast. He's the driver you will have to watch out for, Woody."

"The only place Woody will watch Brian from is the stands," said someone in back of them. "You can't even qualify, can you, Woody?"

They all looked around and there was Buck Brown watching them. "Are you people still here?" Buck went on. "I thought for sure you had left by now."

"Run on back to your pit, Buck," said Mr. House. "Some of us are busy."

"Hey, Buck," called Woody. "How do you like working in the pits?"

When Buck had gone, Mr. House said, "Don't let him get you down, Woody. He wants to make you angry so you won't do well in your qualifying run."

"I know he does," said Woody. "I won't let him worry me. He's not even driving."

Now they could hear the loudspeaker say, "Brian Mahoney qualifies at 193.35 miles an hour. This is the fastest time turned in so far!" Reporters were waiting for Mahoney when he pulled into the pit. There was a large crowd waiting in the pit area to cheer for him.

Woody tried not to think about his last chance to qualify the next day. He knew that everyone in the pit was thinking about it. As they were putting the Queen Bee away in Gasoline Alley for the night, Mahoney came by, stopped, and looked in. He walked over to the Queen Bee.

"You made good time today on your qualifying laps," said Mr. House.

"Thanks, House. Yes, I did," said Mahoney. "That time should give me pole position in the lineup. Too bad you probably won't qualify, Woody. I would have liked to have beaten you in the race. I'll bet you've found out now that this is not like road racing."

"I am not out," said Woody. "I have one more chance."

As they drove back to town, Woody could not help thinking that maybe Mahoney and Buck were right. Maybe he would never make a good "Indy" driver.

8

The Qualifying Laps

Everyone was at the track early the next morning. Woody wanted to do a few practice laps before he did his qualifying laps. The Queen Bee was running good, but Woody was too nervous. If he didn't qualify today, they would all have to go back and never know how the Queen Bee would do in the "500".

When Woody came in after his practice run, they got the Queen Bee ready for the qualifying laps. They took the fuel out of the car and put a more powerful fuel in it. They had been testing to try to get the best octane mixture for high speeds in their car. Almost every pit crew mixed a powerful fuel to use for the qualifying laps. These fuels were hard on the engines, but they helped give the car the extra speed needed to qualify for a good position in the lineup.

Suddenly, it began to rain. The rain would slow the car down and make it harder to go fast enough to qualify.

"Tap," said Mr. House. "Run over and ask the officials if we can put off our last qualifying run. Woody can't make good time in this rain."

Tap ran off for the official's stand while the crew that was left worked over the car. Woody's qualifying laps were to come up in a little while if they were not able to get another time for them.

Tap came running right back. "The officials said that we can wait until tomorrow if the rain doesn't stop," he said.

"I hope the rain stops before then because I'm ready to take it today," said Woody. They all walked around and watched it rain. A little after an hour, Woody thought he would just have to wait until tomorrow.

Then the rain stopped. "That is one thing about Indianapolis," said Mr. House. "It stops raining just as fast as it starts. The Queen Bee is ready. Take it out on the track, Woody."

Woody drove over and waited for the flagman to signal that the track was open. There was still rain on the track, but Woody could do a few warm up laps before doing his qualifying laps. Maybe some of the rain would dry off the track by that time.

Now the flagman dropped his flag, and Woody roared out on the track. At first the rain on the track slowed him down in the turns. The track was starting to dry out.

After three warm-up laps, Woody put his hand up as he passed the timer. Now he would be timed for his next four laps. Woody felt that he would be letting everyone down if he could not qualify today. He knew he could do it.

When Woody came down the straightaway in front of the timer, the car was doing over 195 miles per hour. Woody had never driven this fast before.

Woody knew all of his cutoff places and the fastest way around each turn. The Queen Bee stayed on the track around the turns almost as if it were fastened to the track.

Woody opened the car up again as he went into the straightaway on the back side of the track. On each lap Woody could go a little faster. He felt that he was doing better on these laps than he had done on his other qualifying laps. He felt he was getting the best from the Offy.

At the next turn, Woody knew that he was taking the turns faster than he had ever taken them before. He cut the corners a little more than he had been doing and hit some water on the track.

There was water all over the Queen Bee and all over the shield on his helmet. Woody could not see ahead. He could not tell where the turn was or where the wall was around the track. Woody could not see when he should come out of his drift. He would have to "take the corner blind."

Woody had taken this turn so many times that he gave the car more fuel when he thought he was through the turn. Now he roared down the little straight piece of track before he came to the next turn. The speed of the car blew the water off his helmet shield.

Woody could see through the shield some as he went around this turn and down in front of the stands. This was his last lap. He opened it up all the way and streaked across the finish line. He did one lap to slow down and pulled into the pits.

Everyone came running up to the car. "How did it go?" they all asked.

"I think it went all right," said Woody. "But I had some trouble on the last lap when I ran through some water on the track. That may have slowed me down."

Just then they could hear the loudspeaker, "Woody Woods qualifies at 170.65 mph."

9

Memorial Day

This was Memorial Day, the day of one of the biggest sporting events of the year. Jeff and Tap had stayed all night in Gasoline Alley by the Queen Bee. They didn't want anyone to come around the car before the race. Some of the pit crews who were having trouble with their race cars worked all night.

Mr. House made Woody go to sleep early. Woody tried to sleep, but most of the night he kept thinking about driving the "500" against Brian Mahoney. Woody was nervous about the race.

Ann, Woody, and Mr. House drove out to the track early. Cars were lined up for miles to get into the big race. They had started letting people into the stands at four that morning. The stands would already be filled by eight o'clock.

When they got to Gasoline Alley, they found Jeff and Tap waiting for them. "We were afraid you couldn't get through all of those people," said Tap.

"We made it O.K.," said Mr. House. "Is the car ready to go?"

"That car has been ready to go for weeks," said Jeff.

In the pit they set up everything they might need for the pit stops. They needed many tires because the tires would have to be changed about three times in the 500 mile long race. Each one on the pit crew had a special job to do and had everything in place so he could help get the car back out on the track in a few seconds.

The Queen Bee had jacks in it so no other jacks would be needed to change tires. They would only have a few seconds to jack the car up, change the tires, put fuel in the car, wipe off the face shield, and give Woody something to eat or drink.

When everything was ready in the pits, there was nothing to do but wait for the race to start. Woody walked up and down. If only the race would start. He was always nervous before a race. What if the car should spin out? What if his car should be hit by another car? What if he could not even get the car started? What if?...?

Mr. House talked with Woody about the things they would tell him while he was racing. They would use a big board for this. They would put on the board things like how many laps were finished, Woody's average speed, when to slow down or speed up, when to come in for a pit stop, and what place he would be running.

The Queen Bee was in pit 25 because Woody had placed 25 in the lineup. Buck Brown and Brian Mahoney came by on their way to the first pit. Mahoney had placed pole position in the lineup.

Mahoney stopped when he saw Woody and the others in the pit. "You are about as far down the line as you can be and still be in the race," he said. "You should be in pit 33."

"Go ahead and talk all you want to now," said Woody. "You won't have so much to say after the race."

"I'll say the same thing after the race that I have been saying all the time," said Mahoney. "A road racer is lost in a big race like this. You just don't have it, Woody, boy."

"We will see," said Woody. "I've come too far to turn back now."

After Mahoney and Buck had gone, Mr. House told Woody how to run the race. They began to talk over their plan to win.

"Take it easy for the first part of the race," said Mr. House. "It is a hot day and the cars will start to drop out. Wait until there are not so many cars on the track. There will be so many cars in the race at first that it will be hard to pass. I will tell you when to speed up and when to keep your speed down. I'll tell you when to hold your position and when to move out."

Now there was a big bang. This was the signal that it was almost time for the race to start. Woody felt strange because in a little while he would be driving in his first "500." Woody tried not to think about all the people who were counting on him. He just had to think about staying in the race.

Everything was now ready in the pits. Only five men could work in the pits. Two helpers would stand in back of the wall and give them tools or parts if they were needed. Only the tires to be used in tire changes could be in the pits, no other parts.

Men were cleaning the track now. Anything on the track could hurt a thin racing tire and maybe cause the car to crash. Woody looked at the other drivers as he waited for the race to begin. All the drivers were ready, and standing by their cars. Woody looked at them and felt like he was the only one who was scared and nervous.

"You had better get in," said Mr. House. Something in the way he talked made Woody look at him. Now Woody could see that Mr. House was afraid, too. When he looked at Jeff, Tap, and Ann, they didn't look any better. Woody put on his helmet, snapped on his shield, and slid down into the Queen Bee. Jeff brought up the starter to be ready to start the car. No one said anything.

Now they could hear an official say, "Gentlemen, start your engines."

There was a r-r-r-r-r-r-r-r-o-o-o-o-o-o-m! as the powerful engine on the Queen Bee roared. From every pit there came a roar as 33 cars were started for the big race.

Woody waited in the pits until it was his turn and then moved into his place in the starting lineup. The first lap would be a lap for the people to look at the cars and drivers. There were eleven rows of three cars each. The Queen Bee was in the ninth row.

A big, new, yellow Catalina pace car was in front of the race cars as they did this lap. Then they did a faster lap for the cars to pick up speed. The race cars had to stay in the same places as in the lineup. By the time they came around in front of the stands again, they were doing 100 miles an hour. The yellow car pulled off the track and there was a R-R-R-R-R-R-R-R-R-O-O-O-O-O-O-O-O-M-M-M as 33 cars zoomed ahead.

Woody zoomed ahead to try to get to the front. Everyone did the same thing. Woody thought about what Mr. House had said about holding back for the first part of the race and dropped back. There were a few crashes at the start of the race when everyone was trying to pass. Woody wanted to save the Lotus for the race ahead.

As the cars went around the first turn, Woody could see Mahoney ahead of all the other cars. He was picking up speed. It would be hard for anyone to pass him. But someone had to try.

Cars began to pass Woody. Now he was almost last as they went into the straightaway on the other side of the stands. The drivers in this race were out to win. There is over $250,000 dollars at stake for the winner. He would have to drive as he had never driven before or he would be in last place before long. As the cars came to the last turn before the straightaway, the four cars in front were all trying to get around the turn at the same time. No one wanted to let the others pass.

At the last second, two of the cars tried to slow down and drop in back of the others. It was too late. The first car on the right hit the wall. It came back and hit the other two cars just as they were passing it. The only car of the four to get by was Brian Mahoney, on the inside. Woody and the other cars in the rear could get by and did not hit any of the cars in the crash.

"That is one way I don't want to drop out of this race," said Woody. As he raced by the accident, he could see flames. Two of the drivers were hurt. Woody felt very strange when he saw that scene.

The yellow flag was out now. Woody and all the other drivers would have to slow down to 80 mph and keep the same places in the race until the cars that were in the crash were cleared off the track. For a few seconds, Woody was scared. He knew that it could have been him in the crash.

10

Driving the "500"

The race was in lap 26 now. A few cars were already out of the race. The hot day was hard on the engines and the drivers. As Woody zipped by his pit this time, he could see a big PL 15 on the board. This told him his place in the race. He was trying to keep this place for now. He had passed some cars but was taking it easy and waiting for the last part of the race, when there would not be so many cars on the track. Mahoney was still in the lead. He was driving very well. Mahoney was giving up ground to no one. He would be tough to beat.

Woody was getting used to this race now. The roar of the cars on the track was so loud that he was glad he put ear plugs in place before the race to cut out some of the noise.

Lap after lap passed in this way. Woody worked on cutting the corners a little faster and making a little better lap time each time. The next time he roared by the pits there was a big 155 mph on the board. Woody knew that his last lap time had been 155 miles an hour. Woody was watching his tires, too, to see how they were holding up. Most drivers must make three pit stops for tires and fuel in the race. A driver could make better time if he could cut the pit stops to two.

As Woody went by on lap 60, he could see that Tap had put IN on the board. Woody put his hand up as he saw the board. His tires were about gone. He was ready for pit stop.

It was getting very hot in the cockpit. The track and the engine were hot, and the driving helmet did not cool him off any.

Woody pulled into the pit stop after the next lap. While the pit crew went smoothly to work, one of the crewmen handed Woody a new shield to snap onto his helmet.

Woody felt the car jerk up as the jacks went to work. He heard a bang, bang as Jeff, Tap, and one of the crewmen changed the tires. The other crewman was putting in the fuel and had to be careful not to spill any on the outside of the car. The heat of the car could cause the fuel to catch fire or explode.

When his tires were changed, Jeff gave the windshield a fast cleaning. Woody could hear someone banging the back of the car as a signal that the car was ready to go again. Woody roared back out on the track. He had not said anything to the pit crew because they would not be able to hear him over the roar of the engine.

The pit stop had been quick. It had only lasted for 20 seconds, but it had been long enough for Woody to drop back to 20th place. Woody could make this up when the other cars made their pit stops. Woody began to drive faster. It was time to try to pull up a little on the cars in front of him.

Lap after lap went by. In front, Mahoney and a yellow McNamera were changing places. First one car was ahead and then the other. Woody was slowly picking up speed and passing some slower cars. After 25 more laps Woody's car was in eleventh place.

A black Offy zoomed up behind Woody now. Woody stayed ahead of it for two laps. The driver of the black Offy was going very fast. He tried to pass Woody on one turn. Woody stayed ahead of him. On the next turn the Offy almost forced Woody into the wall. Woody slowed down and let the Offy get ahead. There was going to be a crash, and both cars would be out of the race if the driver of the Offy went on driving like that. As the black Offy went ahead of Woody on the straightaway, Woody pulled up right behind him. The speed of the black car helped pull Woody along and he was able to save gas. He saw the Offy go by two more cars.

"That car is going to be in trouble," thought Woody to himself. "I'll let him get ahead. I don't want to be behind him if there is trouble."

Four laps later Woody knew he had done the right thing. On a turn the black Offy had hit the wall and bounced back and hit another car. These two cars went into a spin and hit two more cars.

STP

There were not so many cars on the race track now. The race was about half over. Many cars had dropped out with engine trouble. Others had been in crashes. Woody saw that there were only four cars in front of him now. The four cars were all trying to get into first place. Woody thought that the best thing to do was to stay right behind them and maybe some of them would drop out.

Lap after lap went by this way. Woody began to feel very tired and hot. At these speeds a driver could not let up for a second. After 140 laps Tap signalled for Woody to come in for another pit stop. He pulled quickly into the pits.

This pit stop was faster than the first one had been. Woody was back out on the track in 17 seconds. Only one tire needed changing. His tires were lasting longer than the crew had thought they would. Woody would have to make one more pit stop. That would be his last.

Woody roared back out on the track to try to make up for time he had lost on the pit stop. In two more laps, two of the cars that were in front of Woody had to go in for pit stops. There were only two cars ahead of Woody for the time being. He would do his best to hold on to this place when the two cars came back out on the track.

Woody held his place behind the first two cars. Woody had been so busy driving that he had not thought about Mahoney for a while. Mahoney had not forgotten about Woody. On one turn Woody almost passed Mahoney as they went around a turn. Woody saw Mahoney look over at him when Mahoney saw the car that was pulling up next to his. Mahoney had never thought that a road race driver would be this close to him in this race with only 50 laps to go.

Mahoney gave his car all the fuel it would take and roared ahead of Woody. Woody fell third behind Mahoney's McLaren and the Johnny Lightning special in second place. He could wait. Lap after lap was run with the cars in the same places.

All the drivers were very tired now, but still the race went on. The cars were all holding the same places. Everyone was too tired to try any harder. All the drivers were waiting for the last part of the race. The first three cars had only made two pit stops each. All the people in the stands were waiting for them to make their last pit stops.

Now the Johnny Lightning Special went into the pit for the last time. The tires on this car were getting too thin. Woody looked at his tires. There were about 25 laps to go. In a little while he should make a stop.

Woody was sure Mahoney was waiting for him to stop. Mahoney wanted to stay in first place at all costs.

The car in second place had made a long, long pit stop. Only after the race did Woody find out why the driver of that car took so long. The driver of the second place car was trying to get back on the track so fast that he had let his engine stop while leaving the pit. Then the pit crew had to get the starter to get the engine going again. This took so long that this car dropped way behind.

Woody's brown Offy and Mahoney's black McLaren stayed in the same position for ten laps. Each driver was waiting for the other driver to go into the pits. Woody looked at his tires again. He checked his fuel supply. If he went into the pits, Mahoney would win the race.

When Woody went by the pits the next time, he signalled that he was not going to make a pit stop. He would have to wait until the next lap to see what Mr. House thought about this. The next time around, Woody saw a big O.K. on the board.

Now Woody gave it all he had. Mahoney saw Woody coming and was not going to let him pass. When Woody went to the right, Mahoney moved to the right. When Woody cut to the left, Mahoney swung to the left.

Lap after lap passed. There were only ten laps to go, then nine. Woody could see that there was no chance of passing by Mahoney. Now there were only three laps left, then two, and at last the last lap.

By the last lap, Woody was watching his tires and thinking that his fuel must almost be gone. One of his tires could go at any second or he could run out of fuel before he finished. As they came down the track in front of the stands, Woody could hear the people even over the roar of the engines and the plugs in his ears. This was it. He had to make a decision, now."

"I've got to chance it," thought Woody, giving the Offenhauser all the fuel it could take. Mahoney did the same thing trying to stay ahead of Woody. Before he knew it, Woody found that he was zooming by Mahoney. What had happened?

It all happened so fast. There was a checkered flag. The people were standing and cheering, but for whom? Brian Mahoney or Woody Woods? Woody did not think that he could have come in first.

As Woody drove around the track again, he saw Mahoney. He was in front of the stands pushing his car to the finish line. If he could get over the finish line by himself, he could still place.

As Woody brought his car to a stop, people came running up to him. Everyone wanted to talk to him. All he saw were hands, arms, faces, microphones, cameras and flowers. Mr. House, Ann, Jeff, and Tap were there somewhere. All Woody wanted to do was to get out of the car. He was hot and very stiff from sitting so long. He wanted to find Mr. House and Ann. He could not believe he won at 'Indy.'

A reporter wanted Woody to say something to the people watching on T.V. All Woody could say was, "I wouldn't be here if it were not for the work of Mr. House and the others in the crew. And I don't think anyone can say now that a road race driver can't make it at the Indianapolis 500!" Everyone cheered.

That night they all came back to the track clubhouse for a big dinner and a party for all the drivers and their crews. After the dinner, the trophies were given out. There were also speeches made by some famous people in the world of sports. They all talked about how great it was this year to have a rookie win the Indianapolis 500, which was one of the biggest sporting events of the year. They said that Woody had proved to everyone that a road racer from a small town could compete with the big name drivers and win.

After the speeches were over, different newspaper writers came up to Woody's table and asked him many questions. They asked him how it felt to win. They asked how he felt about beating Brian "Goggles" Mahoney. They asked him if he and Mr. House had planned to win any certain way. They asked Mr. House, who was sitting with Woody, if the House Racing Co. was going to take Woody and the Queen Bee on the National Tour.

While the writers were talking to Mr. House, Woody slipped away from the crowd and sat down at a table with Tap, Ann, and Jeff.

"Woody," said Tap. "At last we get a chance to talk to you."

"I'm really tired, Tap. I sort of wish these people would leave me alone so I could spend more time with all of you. By the way, have any of you seen Mahoney or Buck?"

"No, Woody," said Jeff. "They're probably still out in the brickyard trying to push that McLaren off the track." Everyone was still laughing when Tap stood up and held out his glass to Woody. "Here's to Woody," he said. "Here's to the grand champion."

"To the grand champion," the others said, as they sipped from their glasses.

"To the grand road racer," added Jeff.

How the "500" Started

Until 1909 races for cars were run on the roads or on tracks that were not very long. A man named Carl Fisher and some of his friends thought that a big track was needed. A big race track would give the men who made cars a place to test them in long races.

These men started the Indianapolis Motor Speedway Company and made a 2½ mile long track at Indianapolis. The first race

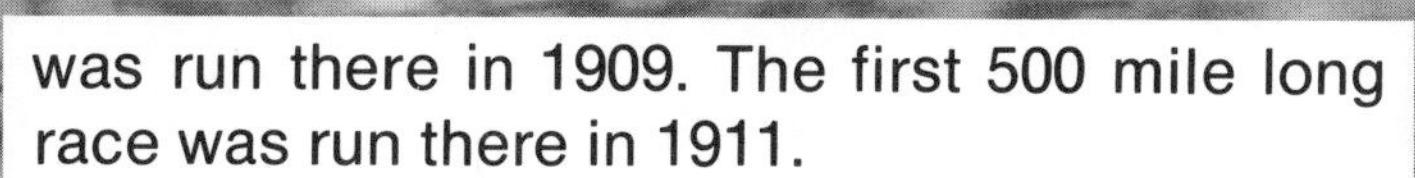

was run there in 1909. The first 500 mile long race was run there in 1911.

The first "500" was won by Ray Harroun. His average speed for a lap in this race was 74.59 miles an hour, and it took him 6:42 hours to finish the race. The average lap speed needed to win this race today is over 160 miles an hour. It only takes half as long for the cars to finish this race today as it did for them to finish the first one.

The Track

The 2½ mile long track was all covered with bricks at one time. It was found that the bricks were very hard on the racing tires and so the track was covered over with asphalt. There is still a strip of bricks in front of the stands so the people can see how the track looked at one time. A wall around the track helps to keep the race cars from hitting people who are working in the pits or watching the race.

At the Indianapolis Speedway there are big stands for the many people who come from all over to see the races. The places where the garages for the race cars are is known as Gasoline Alley. Everything that anyone could ever need to fix a race car can be found in Gasoline Alley.

When the cars are racing, they are worked on in the pits. This is just an open place off the track that the drivers can drive into. At one time the place where race cars were worked on was a place dug into the ground so it was called a pit. It is still called a pit now even though it is on the same level as the track.

At the Speedway there is anything the men who work on cars could need. There are places to eat, and even a nine hole golf course. The track runs around the course.

The Cars

The cars that race at the Indianapolis "500" are made for that kind of racing only. They are weighted on the left side and will turn left only.

Most cars at the "500" have either four cylinder turbocharged Offenhauser engines or turbocharged Ford V-8 engines in them. For the race in 1967 the STP Corporation built a fast machine called a turbocar. In it was a turbine engine made for small jet planes and helicopters. The USAC later made this kind of car illegal to race at "Indy" because it was *too* fast. The USAC believed that the turbocar had too much of an advantage over the other cars at Indy.

The fuel used in most of these racing cars is methanol. Some drivers and pit crews put other things in the methanol to give their cars more power. The race cars are started with an electric starter that can be moved up when needed. The cars cannot be re-started without the electric starter.

The rubber on the racing tires is very thin because the fast speeds of the race make the tires get very hot. The thin layer of rubber on the tires makes it easier for the heat to get out so the tire will not blow up. These thin layers of rubber do not let the tire last very long.

The Drivers

Drivers have to be 21 years old to drive in the "500". They must pass a physical test and a driving test before they can race at Indianapolis. There are four parts to the driving test. A driver does ten laps each at speeds of 140, 145, 150, and 155 miles per hour. His speed can be one mile an hour under the right speed, or four miles an hour above it. If his speed if off any more than that, he does not pass his test. Track officials watch from places on the track to see how the new driver does.

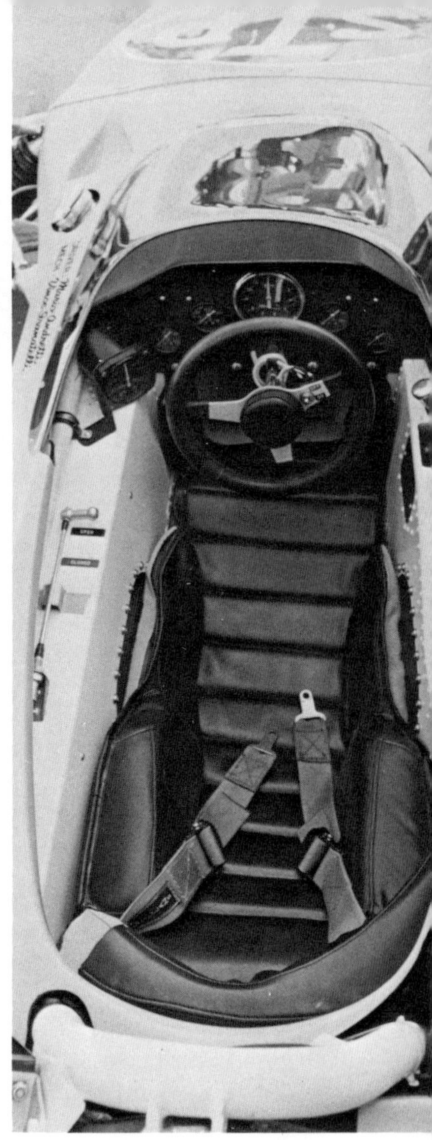

A driver must use the following things at all times when he is driving:
A helmet (with face shield) and a fireproof racing suit, a padded seat, seat belt, and shoulder harness.

Many drivers put plugs in their ears before a race to cut out some of the noise. The roar of the many powerful engines can hurt the driver's ears. Many drivers also wear hoods under their helmets for added protection from the noise.

The Race

Qualification runs are made before the race. Each car has three chances to qualify. In each qualifying run, the car does four laps and the average time for the laps is used to see if the driver is fast enough to be in the race. The 33 cars with the fastest times are in the race. The fastest car will be in the first inside row which is thought to be the best place in the race. This place is called the *pole position*. Cars are placed in eleven rows, three cars each. The faster cars are in the front.

At the beginning of the race, the cars in their rows stay in back of the pace car. The first lap is for the people to look at the cars and the next lap is the pace lap.

The pit crew works with the driver all through the race by holding up a large blackboard which tells him how many laps he has to go, what his average speed is, whether to speed up or slow down, what place he is in, and when to come in for a pit stop.

Five of the crew can be in the pit when their car is in the pit. The other two stay in back of the wall and hand them things they need. Pit stops can be dangerous. Fire extinguishers must be ready when the car is getting fuel (see picture). The engine is very hot and can not be turned off because it would take too much time to start it again.

The driver and the pit crew help each other. A race car driver can not win a race if he does not have a good pit crew in back of him.

Acknowledgements

Kenneth Shields - Illustrations

Special thanks for help provided by:

Indianapolis Motor Speedway Corporation
pages 70, 71, 73, 78

STP Corporation, pages 75, 76

Hot Rod - Woody Woods wants more than anything to own a hot rod and enter it in the hot rod derby. Buck Brown and his friends have other plans for Woody.

Destruction Derby - Woody Woods needs some money so he can buy parts to make his hot rod even faster on the track. The $300.00 prize makes the Derby a "must" for Woody.

Drag Race - Woody's hot rod, the Bumble Bee, is fast, but not fast enough to beat Buck Brown in the Drag Races. With the help of a strange new friend, Woody makes his hot rod even faster. But is it?

The Stock Car Race - Woody's interest in cars leads him to Mr. House's racing shop, and a chance to work on real stock cars. Woody learns something from a pretty visitor, and gets his chance to race a stock car.

Road Race - Woody Woods, while driving a high powered Lotus in a road race, is in an accident. His hands badly burned and his leg broken, he says he will never drive again. He gets over much of his fear, but it is on the day of the big road race that he must make a big decision.

Indy 500 - The Indy 500 is the toughest test of car and driver. Few drivers who begin the race finish it. Woody Woods has something to prove to himself and to his friends: that a "road race" driver can win at Indianapolis.